THIS BOOK BELONGS TO:

CONTACT INFORMATION	
NAME	
ADDRESS	
PHONE #	
EMAIL	

DEDICATION

This Vinyl Collection Log Book is dedicated to people who want to document and organize their record collection.

You are my inspiration for producing this book and I'm honored to be a part of tracking and managing your record collection.

HOW TO USE THIS BOOK

This Vinyl Record Log Book will allow you to accurately record every detail of your collection. It's a great way to organize and catalog the details of your vinyl collection.

Here are examples of information for you to fill in and write the details about your experience in this book.

Fill in the following information:

1. Record Details - Fill in the name of the album, artist, country, year, format, catalog number, record label, grade price, and liner notes.

2. Notes - Space to write extra details of your collection.

RECORD DETAILS

ALBUM		CATALOG #	
ARTIST		LABEL	
COUNTRY		GRADE	
YEAR		PRICE	
FORMAT		LINER NOTES	

NOTES

RECORD DETAILS

ALBUM		CATALOG #	
ARTIST		LABEL	
COUNTRY		GRADE	
YEAR		PRICE	
FORMAT		LINER NOTES	

NOTES

RECORD DETAILS

ALBUM		CATALOG #	
ARTIST		LABEL	
COUNTRY		GRADE	
YEAR		PRICE	
FORMAT		LINER NOTES	

NOTES

RECORD DETAILS

ALBUM		CATALOG #	
ARTIST		LABEL	
COUNTRY		GRADE	
YEAR		PRICE	
FORMAT		LINER NOTES	

NOTES

RECORD DETAILS

ALBUM		CATALOG #	
ARTIST		LABEL	
COUNTRY		GRADE	
YEAR		PRICE	
FORMAT		LINER NOTES	

NOTES

RECORD DETAILS

ALBUM		CATALOG #	
ARTIST		LABEL	
COUNTRY		GRADE	
YEAR		PRICE	
FORMAT		LINER NOTES	

NOTES

RECORD DETAILS

ALBUM		CATALOG #	
ARTIST		LABEL	
COUNTRY		GRADE	
YEAR		PRICE	
FORMAT		LINER NOTES	

NOTES

RECORD DETAILS

ALBUM		CATALOG #	
ARTIST		LABEL	
COUNTRY		GRADE	
YEAR		PRICE	
FORMAT		LINER NOTES	

NOTES

RECORD DETAILS

ALBUM		CATALOG #	
ARTIST		LABEL	
COUNTRY		GRADE	
YEAR		PRICE	
FORMAT		LINER NOTES	

NOTES

RECORD DETAILS

ALBUM		CATALOG #	
ARTIST		LABEL	
COUNTRY		GRADE	
YEAR		PRICE	
FORMAT		LINER NOTES	

NOTES

RECORD DETAILS

ALBUM		CATALOG #	
ARTIST		LABEL	
COUNTRY		GRADE	
YEAR		PRICE	
FORMAT		LINER NOTES	

NOTES

RECORD DETAILS

ALBUM		CATALOG #	
ARTIST		LABEL	
COUNTRY		GRADE	
YEAR		PRICE	
FORMAT		LINER NOTES	

NOTES

RECORD DETAILS

ALBUM		CATALOG #	
ARTIST		LABEL	
COUNTRY		GRADE	
YEAR		PRICE	
FORMAT		LINER NOTES	

NOTES

RECORD DETAILS

ALBUM		CATALOG #	
ARTIST		LABEL	
COUNTRY		GRADE	
YEAR		PRICE	
FORMAT		LINER NOTES	

NOTES

RECORD DETAILS

ALBUM		CATALOG #	
ARTIST		LABEL	
COUNTRY		GRADE	
YEAR		PRICE	
FORMAT		LINER NOTES	

NOTES

RECORD DETAILS

ALBUM		CATALOG #	
ARTIST		LABEL	
COUNTRY		GRADE	
YEAR		PRICE	
FORMAT		LINER NOTES	

NOTES

RECORD DETAILS

ALBUM		CATALOG #	
ARTIST		LABEL	
COUNTRY		GRADE	
YEAR		PRICE	
FORMAT		LINER NOTES	

NOTES

RECORD DETAILS

ALBUM		CATALOG #	
ARTIST		LABEL	
COUNTRY		GRADE	
YEAR		PRICE	
FORMAT		LINER NOTES	

NOTES

RECORD DETAILS

ALBUM		CATALOG #	
ARTIST		LABEL	
COUNTRY		GRADE	
YEAR		PRICE	
FORMAT		LINER NOTES	

NOTES

RECORD DETAILS

ALBUM		CATALOG #	
ARTIST		LABEL	
COUNTRY		GRADE	
YEAR		PRICE	
FORMAT		LINER NOTES	

NOTES

RECORD DETAILS

ALBUM		CATALOG #	
ARTIST		LABEL	
COUNTRY		GRADE	
YEAR		PRICE	
FORMAT		LINER NOTES	

NOTES

RECORD DETAILS

ALBUM		CATALOG #	
ARTIST		LABEL	
COUNTRY		GRADE	
YEAR		PRICE	
FORMAT		LINER NOTES	

NOTES

RECORD DETAILS

ALBUM		CATALOG #	
ARTIST		LABEL	
COUNTRY		GRADE	
YEAR		PRICE	
FORMAT		LINER NOTES	

NOTES

RECORD DETAILS

ALBUM		CATALOG #	
ARTIST		LABEL	
COUNTRY		GRADE	
YEAR		PRICE	
FORMAT		LINER NOTES	

NOTES

RECORD DETAILS

ALBUM		CATALOG #	
ARTIST		LABEL	
COUNTRY		GRADE	
YEAR		PRICE	
FORMAT		LINER NOTES	

NOTES

RECORD DETAILS

ALBUM		CATALOG #	
ARTIST		LABEL	
COUNTRY		GRADE	
YEAR		PRICE	
FORMAT		LINER NOTES	

NOTES

RECORD DETAILS

ALBUM		CATALOG #	
ARTIST		LABEL	
COUNTRY		GRADE	
YEAR		PRICE	
FORMAT		LINER NOTES	

NOTES

RECORD DETAILS

ALBUM		CATALOG #	
ARTIST		LABEL	
COUNTRY		GRADE	
YEAR		PRICE	
FORMAT		LINER NOTES	

NOTES

RECORD DETAILS

ALBUM		CATALOG #	
ARTIST		LABEL	
COUNTRY		GRADE	
YEAR		PRICE	
FORMAT		LINER NOTES	

NOTES

RECORD DETAILS

ALBUM		CATALOG #	
ARTIST		LABEL	
COUNTRY		GRADE	
YEAR		PRICE	
FORMAT		LINER NOTES	

NOTES

RECORD DETAILS

ALBUM		CATALOG #	
ARTIST		LABEL	
COUNTRY		GRADE	
YEAR		PRICE	
FORMAT		LINER NOTES	

NOTES

RECORD DETAILS

ALBUM		CATALOG #	
ARTIST		LABEL	
COUNTRY		GRADE	
YEAR		PRICE	
FORMAT		LINER NOTES	

NOTES

RECORD DETAILS

ALBUM		CATALOG #	
ARTIST		LABEL	
COUNTRY		GRADE	
YEAR		PRICE	
FORMAT		LINER NOTES	

NOTES

RECORD DETAILS

ALBUM		CATALOG #	
ARTIST		LABEL	
COUNTRY		GRADE	
YEAR		PRICE	
FORMAT		LINER NOTES	

NOTES

RECORD DETAILS

ALBUM		CATALOG #	
ARTIST		LABEL	
COUNTRY		GRADE	
YEAR		PRICE	
FORMAT		LINER NOTES	

NOTES

RECORD DETAILS

ALBUM		CATALOG #	
ARTIST		LABEL	
COUNTRY		GRADE	
YEAR		PRICE	
FORMAT		LINER NOTES	

NOTES

RECORD DETAILS

ALBUM		CATALOG #	
ARTIST		LABEL	
COUNTRY		GRADE	
YEAR		PRICE	
FORMAT		LINER NOTES	

NOTES

RECORD DETAILS

ALBUM		CATALOG #	
ARTIST		LABEL	
COUNTRY		GRADE	
YEAR		PRICE	
FORMAT		LINER NOTES	

NOTES

RECORD DETAILS

ALBUM		CATALOG #	
ARTIST		LABEL	
COUNTRY		GRADE	
YEAR		PRICE	
FORMAT		LINER NOTES	

NOTES

RECORD DETAILS

ALBUM		CATALOG #	
ARTIST		LABEL	
COUNTRY		GRADE	
YEAR		PRICE	
FORMAT		LINER NOTES	

NOTES

RECORD DETAILS

ALBUM		CATALOG #	
ARTIST		LABEL	
COUNTRY		GRADE	
YEAR		PRICE	
FORMAT		LINER NOTES	

NOTES

RECORD DETAILS

ALBUM		CATALOG #	
ARTIST		LABEL	
COUNTRY		GRADE	
YEAR		PRICE	
FORMAT		LINER NOTES	

NOTES

RECORD DETAILS

ALBUM		CATALOG #	
ARTIST		LABEL	
COUNTRY		GRADE	
YEAR		PRICE	
FORMAT		LINER NOTES	

NOTES

RECORD DETAILS

ALBUM		CATALOG #	
ARTIST		LABEL	
COUNTRY		GRADE	
YEAR		PRICE	
FORMAT		LINER NOTES	

NOTES

RECORD DETAILS

ALBUM		CATALOG #	
ARTIST		LABEL	
COUNTRY		GRADE	
YEAR		PRICE	
FORMAT		LINER NOTES	

NOTES

RECORD DETAILS

ALBUM		CATALOG #	
ARTIST		LABEL	
COUNTRY		GRADE	
YEAR		PRICE	
FORMAT		LINER NOTES	

NOTES

RECORD DETAILS

ALBUM		CATALOG #	
ARTIST		LABEL	
COUNTRY		GRADE	
YEAR		PRICE	
FORMAT		LINER NOTES	

NOTES

RECORD DETAILS

ALBUM		CATALOG #	
ARTIST		LABEL	
COUNTRY		GRADE	
YEAR		PRICE	
FORMAT		LINER NOTES	

NOTES

RECORD DETAILS

ALBUM		CATALOG #	
ARTIST		LABEL	
COUNTRY		GRADE	
YEAR		PRICE	
FORMAT		LINER NOTES	

NOTES

RECORD DETAILS

ALBUM		CATALOG #	
ARTIST		LABEL	
COUNTRY		GRADE	
YEAR		PRICE	
FORMAT		LINER NOTES	

NOTES

RECORD DETAILS

ALBUM		CATALOG #	
ARTIST		LABEL	
COUNTRY		GRADE	
YEAR		PRICE	
FORMAT		LINER NOTES	

NOTES

RECORD DETAILS

ALBUM		CATALOG #	
ARTIST		LABEL	
COUNTRY		GRADE	
YEAR		PRICE	
FORMAT		LINER NOTES	

NOTES

RECORD DETAILS

ALBUM		CATALOG #	
ARTIST		LABEL	
COUNTRY		GRADE	
YEAR		PRICE	
FORMAT		LINER NOTES	

NOTES

RECORD DETAILS

ALBUM		CATALOG #	
ARTIST		LABEL	
COUNTRY		GRADE	
YEAR		PRICE	
FORMAT		LINER NOTES	

NOTES

RECORD DETAILS

ALBUM		CATALOG #	
ARTIST		LABEL	
COUNTRY		GRADE	
YEAR		PRICE	
FORMAT		LINER NOTES	

NOTES

RECORD DETAILS

ALBUM		CATALOG #	
ARTIST		LABEL	
COUNTRY		GRADE	
YEAR		PRICE	
FORMAT		LINER NOTES	

NOTES

RECORD DETAILS

ALBUM		CATALOG #	
ARTIST		LABEL	
COUNTRY		GRADE	
YEAR		PRICE	
FORMAT		LINER NOTES	

NOTES

RECORD DETAILS

ALBUM		CATALOG #	
ARTIST		LABEL	
COUNTRY		GRADE	
YEAR		PRICE	
FORMAT		LINER NOTES	

NOTES

RECORD DETAILS

ALBUM		CATALOG #	
ARTIST		LABEL	
COUNTRY		GRADE	
YEAR		PRICE	
FORMAT		LINER NOTES	

NOTES

RECORD DETAILS

ALBUM		CATALOG #	
ARTIST		LABEL	
COUNTRY		GRADE	
YEAR		PRICE	
FORMAT		LINER NOTES	

NOTES

RECORD DETAILS

ALBUM		CATALOG #	
ARTIST		LABEL	
COUNTRY		GRADE	
YEAR		PRICE	
FORMAT		LINER NOTES	

NOTES

RECORD DETAILS

ALBUM		CATALOG #	
ARTIST		LABEL	
COUNTRY		GRADE	
YEAR		PRICE	
FORMAT		LINER NOTES	

NOTES

RECORD DETAILS

ALBUM		CATALOG #	
ARTIST		LABEL	
COUNTRY		GRADE	
YEAR		PRICE	
FORMAT		LINER NOTES	

NOTES

RECORD DETAILS

ALBUM		CATALOG #	
ARTIST		LABEL	
COUNTRY		GRADE	
YEAR		PRICE	
FORMAT		LINER NOTES	

NOTES

RECORD DETAILS

ALBUM		CATALOG #	
ARTIST		LABEL	
COUNTRY		GRADE	
YEAR		PRICE	
FORMAT		LINER NOTES	

NOTES

RECORD DETAILS

ALBUM		CATALOG #	
ARTIST		LABEL	
COUNTRY		GRADE	
YEAR		PRICE	
FORMAT		LINER NOTES	

NOTES

RECORD DETAILS

ALBUM		CATALOG #	
ARTIST		LABEL	
COUNTRY		GRADE	
YEAR		PRICE	
FORMAT		LINER NOTES	

NOTES

RECORD DETAILS

ALBUM		CATALOG #	
ARTIST		LABEL	
COUNTRY		GRADE	
YEAR		PRICE	
FORMAT		LINER NOTES	

NOTES

RECORD DETAILS

ALBUM		CATALOG #	
ARTIST		LABEL	
COUNTRY		GRADE	
YEAR		PRICE	
FORMAT		LINER NOTES	

NOTES

RECORD DETAILS

ALBUM		CATALOG #	
ARTIST		LABEL	
COUNTRY		GRADE	
YEAR		PRICE	
FORMAT		LINER NOTES	

NOTES

RECORD DETAILS

ALBUM		CATALOG #	
ARTIST		LABEL	
COUNTRY		GRADE	
YEAR		PRICE	
FORMAT		LINER NOTES	

NOTES

RECORD DETAILS

ALBUM		CATALOG #	
ARTIST		LABEL	
COUNTRY		GRADE	
YEAR		PRICE	
FORMAT		LINER NOTES	

NOTES

RECORD DETAILS

ALBUM		CATALOG #	
ARTIST		LABEL	
COUNTRY		GRADE	
YEAR		PRICE	
FORMAT		LINER NOTES	

NOTES

RECORD DETAILS

ALBUM		CATALOG #	
ARTIST		LABEL	
COUNTRY		GRADE	
YEAR		PRICE	
FORMAT		LINER NOTES	

NOTES

RECORD DETAILS

ALBUM		CATALOG #	
ARTIST		LABEL	
COUNTRY		GRADE	
YEAR		PRICE	
FORMAT		LINER NOTES	

NOTES

RECORD DETAILS

ALBUM		CATALOG #	
ARTIST		LABEL	
COUNTRY		GRADE	
YEAR		PRICE	
FORMAT		LINER NOTES	

NOTES

RECORD DETAILS

ALBUM		CATALOG #	
ARTIST		LABEL	
COUNTRY		GRADE	
YEAR		PRICE	
FORMAT		LINER NOTES	

NOTES

RECORD DETAILS

ALBUM		CATALOG #	
ARTIST		LABEL	
COUNTRY		GRADE	
YEAR		PRICE	
FORMAT		LINER NOTES	

NOTES

RECORD DETAILS

ALBUM		CATALOG #	
ARTIST		LABEL	
COUNTRY		GRADE	
YEAR		PRICE	
FORMAT		LINER NOTES	

NOTES

RECORD DETAILS

ALBUM		CATALOG #	
ARTIST		LABEL	
COUNTRY		GRADE	
YEAR		PRICE	
FORMAT		LINER NOTES	

NOTES

RECORD DETAILS

ALBUM		CATALOG #	
ARTIST		LABEL	
COUNTRY		GRADE	
YEAR		PRICE	
FORMAT		LINER NOTES	

NOTES

RECORD DETAILS

ALBUM		CATALOG #	
ARTIST		LABEL	
COUNTRY		GRADE	
YEAR		PRICE	
FORMAT		LINER NOTES	

NOTES

RECORD DETAILS

ALBUM		CATALOG #	
ARTIST		LABEL	
COUNTRY		GRADE	
YEAR		PRICE	
FORMAT		LINER NOTES	

NOTES

RECORD DETAILS

ALBUM		CATALOG #	
ARTIST		LABEL	
COUNTRY		GRADE	
YEAR		PRICE	
FORMAT		LINER NOTES	

NOTES

RECORD DETAILS

ALBUM		CATALOG #	
ARTIST		LABEL	
COUNTRY		GRADE	
YEAR		PRICE	
FORMAT		LINER NOTES	

NOTES

RECORD DETAILS

ALBUM		CATALOG #	
ARTIST		LABEL	
COUNTRY		GRADE	
YEAR		PRICE	
FORMAT		LINER NOTES	

NOTES

RECORD DETAILS

ALBUM		CATALOG #	
ARTIST		LABEL	
COUNTRY		GRADE	
YEAR		PRICE	
FORMAT		LINER NOTES	

NOTES

RECORD DETAILS

ALBUM		CATALOG #	
ARTIST		LABEL	
COUNTRY		GRADE	
YEAR		PRICE	
FORMAT		LINER NOTES	

NOTES

RECORD DETAILS

ALBUM		CATALOG #	
ARTIST		LABEL	
COUNTRY		GRADE	
YEAR		PRICE	
FORMAT		LINER NOTES	

NOTES

RECORD DETAILS

ALBUM		CATALOG #	
ARTIST		LABEL	
COUNTRY		GRADE	
YEAR		PRICE	
FORMAT		LINER NOTES	

NOTES

RECORD DETAILS

ALBUM		CATALOG #	
ARTIST		LABEL	
COUNTRY		GRADE	
YEAR		PRICE	
FORMAT		LINER NOTES	

NOTES

RECORD DETAILS

ALBUM		CATALOG #	
ARTIST		LABEL	
COUNTRY		GRADE	
YEAR		PRICE	
FORMAT		LINER NOTES	

NOTES

RECORD DETAILS

ALBUM		CATALOG #	
ARTIST		LABEL	
COUNTRY		GRADE	
YEAR		PRICE	
FORMAT		LINER NOTES	

NOTES

RECORD DETAILS

ALBUM		CATALOG #	
ARTIST		LABEL	
COUNTRY		GRADE	
YEAR		PRICE	
FORMAT		LINER NOTES	

NOTES

RECORD DETAILS

ALBUM		CATALOG #	
ARTIST		LABEL	
COUNTRY		GRADE	
YEAR		PRICE	
FORMAT		LINER NOTES	

NOTES

RECORD DETAILS

ALBUM		CATALOG #	
ARTIST		LABEL	
COUNTRY		GRADE	
YEAR		PRICE	
FORMAT		LINER NOTES	

NOTES

RECORD DETAILS

ALBUM		CATALOG #	
ARTIST		LABEL	
COUNTRY		GRADE	
YEAR		PRICE	
FORMAT		LINER NOTES	

NOTES

RECORD DETAILS

ALBUM		CATALOG #	
ARTIST		LABEL	
COUNTRY		GRADE	
YEAR		PRICE	
FORMAT		LINER NOTES	

NOTES

RECORD DETAILS

ALBUM		CATALOG #	
ARTIST		LABEL	
COUNTRY		GRADE	
YEAR		PRICE	
FORMAT		LINER NOTES	

NOTES

RECORD DETAILS

ALBUM		CATALOG #	
ARTIST		LABEL	
COUNTRY		GRADE	
YEAR		PRICE	
FORMAT		LINER NOTES	

NOTES

RECORD DETAILS

ALBUM		CATALOG #	
ARTIST		LABEL	
COUNTRY		GRADE	
YEAR		PRICE	
FORMAT		LINER NOTES	

NOTES

RECORD DETAILS

ALBUM		CATALOG #	
ARTIST		LABEL	
COUNTRY		GRADE	
YEAR		PRICE	
FORMAT		LINER NOTES	

NOTES

RECORD DETAILS

ALBUM		CATALOG #	
ARTIST		LABEL	
COUNTRY		GRADE	
YEAR		PRICE	
FORMAT		LINER NOTES	

NOTES

RECORD DETAILS

ALBUM		CATALOG #	
ARTIST		LABEL	
COUNTRY		GRADE	
YEAR		PRICE	
FORMAT		LINER NOTES	

NOTES

RECORD DETAILS

ALBUM		CATALOG #	
ARTIST		LABEL	
COUNTRY		GRADE	
YEAR		PRICE	
FORMAT		LINER NOTES	

NOTES

RECORD DETAILS

ALBUM		CATALOG #	
ARTIST		LABEL	
COUNTRY		GRADE	
YEAR		PRICE	
FORMAT		LINER NOTES	

NOTES

RECORD DETAILS

ALBUM		CATALOG #	
ARTIST		LABEL	
COUNTRY		GRADE	
YEAR		PRICE	
FORMAT		LINER NOTES	

NOTES

RECORD DETAILS

ALBUM		CATALOG #	
ARTIST		LABEL	
COUNTRY		GRADE	
YEAR		PRICE	
FORMAT		LINER NOTES	

NOTES

RECORD DETAILS

ALBUM		CATALOG #	
ARTIST		LABEL	
COUNTRY		GRADE	
YEAR		PRICE	
FORMAT		LINER NOTES	

NOTES

RECORD DETAILS

ALBUM		CATALOG #	
ARTIST		LABEL	
COUNTRY		GRADE	
YEAR		PRICE	
FORMAT		LINER NOTES	

NOTES

RECORD DETAILS

ALBUM		CATALOG #	
ARTIST		LABEL	
COUNTRY		GRADE	
YEAR		PRICE	
FORMAT		LINER NOTES	

NOTES

RECORD DETAILS

ALBUM		CATALOG #	
ARTIST		LABEL	
COUNTRY		GRADE	
YEAR		PRICE	
FORMAT		LINER NOTES	

NOTES

RECORD DETAILS

ALBUM		CATALOG #	
ARTIST		LABEL	
COUNTRY		GRADE	
YEAR		PRICE	
FORMAT		LINER NOTES	

NOTES

RECORD DETAILS

ALBUM		CATALOG #	
ARTIST		LABEL	
COUNTRY		GRADE	
YEAR		PRICE	
FORMAT		LINER NOTES	

NOTES

RECORD DETAILS

ALBUM		CATALOG #	
ARTIST		LABEL	
COUNTRY		GRADE	
YEAR		PRICE	
FORMAT		LINER NOTES	

NOTES

RECORD DETAILS

ALBUM		CATALOG #	
ARTIST		LABEL	
COUNTRY		GRADE	
YEAR		PRICE	
FORMAT		LINER NOTES	

NOTES

RECORD DETAILS

ALBUM		CATALOG #	
ARTIST		LABEL	
COUNTRY		GRADE	
YEAR		PRICE	
FORMAT		LINER NOTES	

NOTES

RECORD DETAILS

ALBUM		CATALOG #	
ARTIST		LABEL	
COUNTRY		GRADE	
YEAR		PRICE	
FORMAT		LINER NOTES	

NOTES

RECORD DETAILS

ALBUM		CATALOG #	
ARTIST		LABEL	
COUNTRY		GRADE	
YEAR		PRICE	
FORMAT		LINER NOTES	

NOTES

RECORD DETAILS

ALBUM		CATALOG #	
ARTIST		LABEL	
COUNTRY		GRADE	
YEAR		PRICE	
FORMAT		LINER NOTES	

NOTES

RECORD DETAILS

ALBUM		CATALOG #	
ARTIST		LABEL	
COUNTRY		GRADE	
YEAR		PRICE	
FORMAT		LINER NOTES	

NOTES

RECORD DETAILS

ALBUM		CATALOG #	
ARTIST		LABEL	
COUNTRY		GRADE	
YEAR		PRICE	
FORMAT		LINER NOTES	

NOTES

RECORD DETAILS

ALBUM		CATALOG #	
ARTIST		LABEL	
COUNTRY		GRADE	
YEAR		PRICE	
FORMAT		LINER NOTES	

NOTES

RECORD DETAILS

ALBUM		CATALOG #	
ARTIST		LABEL	
COUNTRY		GRADE	
YEAR		PRICE	
FORMAT		LINER NOTES	

NOTES

RECORD DETAILS

ALBUM		CATALOG #	
ARTIST		LABEL	
COUNTRY		GRADE	
YEAR		PRICE	
FORMAT		LINER NOTES	

NOTES

RECORD DETAILS

ALBUM		CATALOG #	
ARTIST		LABEL	
COUNTRY		GRADE	
YEAR		PRICE	
FORMAT		LINER NOTES	

NOTES

RECORD DETAILS

ALBUM		CATALOG #	
ARTIST		LABEL	
COUNTRY		GRADE	
YEAR		PRICE	
FORMAT		LINER NOTES	

NOTES

RECORD DETAILS

ALBUM		CATALOG #	
ARTIST		LABEL	
COUNTRY		GRADE	
YEAR		PRICE	
FORMAT		LINER NOTES	

NOTES

RECORD DETAILS

ALBUM		CATALOG #	
ARTIST		LABEL	
COUNTRY		GRADE	
YEAR		PRICE	
FORMAT		LINER NOTES	

NOTES

RECORD DETAILS

ALBUM		CATALOG #	
ARTIST		LABEL	
COUNTRY		GRADE	
YEAR		PRICE	
FORMAT		LINER NOTES	

NOTES

RECORD DETAILS

ALBUM		CATALOG #	
ARTIST		LABEL	
COUNTRY		GRADE	
YEAR		PRICE	
FORMAT		LINER NOTES	

NOTES

RECORD DETAILS

ALBUM		CATALOG #	
ARTIST		LABEL	
COUNTRY		GRADE	
YEAR		PRICE	
FORMAT		LINER NOTES	

NOTES

RECORD DETAILS

ALBUM		CATALOG #	
ARTIST		LABEL	
COUNTRY		GRADE	
YEAR		PRICE	
FORMAT		LINER NOTES	

NOTES

RECORD DETAILS

ALBUM		CATALOG #	
ARTIST		LABEL	
COUNTRY		GRADE	
YEAR		PRICE	
FORMAT		LINER NOTES	

NOTES

RECORD DETAILS

ALBUM		CATALOG #	
ARTIST		LABEL	
COUNTRY		GRADE	
YEAR		PRICE	
FORMAT		LINER NOTES	

NOTES

RECORD DETAILS

ALBUM		CATALOG #	
ARTIST		LABEL	
COUNTRY		GRADE	
YEAR		PRICE	
FORMAT		LINER NOTES	

NOTES

RECORD DETAILS

ALBUM		CATALOG #	
ARTIST		LABEL	
COUNTRY		GRADE	
YEAR		PRICE	
FORMAT		LINER NOTES	

NOTES

RECORD DETAILS

ALBUM		CATALOG #	
ARTIST		LABEL	
COUNTRY		GRADE	
YEAR		PRICE	
FORMAT		LINER NOTES	

NOTES

RECORD DETAILS

ALBUM		CATALOG #	
ARTIST		LABEL	
COUNTRY		GRADE	
YEAR		PRICE	
FORMAT		LINER NOTES	

NOTES

RECORD DETAILS

ALBUM		CATALOG #	
ARTIST		LABEL	
COUNTRY		GRADE	
YEAR		PRICE	
FORMAT		LINER NOTES	

NOTES

RECORD DETAILS

ALBUM		CATALOG #	
ARTIST		LABEL	
COUNTRY		GRADE	
YEAR		PRICE	
FORMAT		LINER NOTES	

NOTES

RECORD DETAILS

ALBUM		CATALOG #	
ARTIST		LABEL	
COUNTRY		GRADE	
YEAR		PRICE	
FORMAT		LINER NOTES	

NOTES

RECORD DETAILS

ALBUM		CATALOG #	
ARTIST		LABEL	
COUNTRY		GRADE	
YEAR		PRICE	
FORMAT		LINER NOTES	

NOTES

RECORD DETAILS

ALBUM		CATALOG #	
ARTIST		LABEL	
COUNTRY		GRADE	
YEAR		PRICE	
FORMAT		LINER NOTES	

NOTES

RECORD DETAILS

ALBUM		CATALOG #	
ARTIST		LABEL	
COUNTRY		GRADE	
YEAR		PRICE	
FORMAT		LINER NOTES	

NOTES

RECORD DETAILS

ALBUM		CATALOG #	
ARTIST		LABEL	
COUNTRY		GRADE	
YEAR		PRICE	
FORMAT		LINER NOTES	

NOTES

RECORD DETAILS

ALBUM		CATALOG #	
ARTIST		LABEL	
COUNTRY		GRADE	
YEAR		PRICE	
FORMAT		LINER NOTES	

NOTES

RECORD DETAILS

ALBUM		CATALOG #	
ARTIST		LABEL	
COUNTRY		GRADE	
YEAR		PRICE	
FORMAT		LINER NOTES	

NOTES

RECORD DETAILS

ALBUM		CATALOG #	
ARTIST		LABEL	
COUNTRY		GRADE	
YEAR		PRICE	
FORMAT		LINER NOTES	

NOTES

RECORD DETAILS

ALBUM		CATALOG #	
ARTIST		LABEL	
COUNTRY		GRADE	
YEAR		PRICE	
FORMAT		LINER NOTES	

NOTES

RECORD DETAILS

ALBUM		CATALOG #	
ARTIST		LABEL	
COUNTRY		GRADE	
YEAR		PRICE	
FORMAT		LINER NOTES	

NOTES

RECORD DETAILS

ALBUM		CATALOG #	
ARTIST		LABEL	
COUNTRY		GRADE	
YEAR		PRICE	
FORMAT		LINER NOTES	

NOTES

RECORD DETAILS

ALBUM		CATALOG #	
ARTIST		LABEL	
COUNTRY		GRADE	
YEAR		PRICE	
FORMAT		LINER NOTES	

NOTES

RECORD DETAILS

ALBUM		CATALOG #	
ARTIST		LABEL	
COUNTRY		GRADE	
YEAR		PRICE	
FORMAT		LINER NOTES	

NOTES

RECORD DETAILS

ALBUM		CATALOG #	
ARTIST		LABEL	
COUNTRY		GRADE	
YEAR		PRICE	
FORMAT		LINER NOTES	

NOTES

RECORD DETAILS

ALBUM		CATALOG #	
ARTIST		LABEL	
COUNTRY		GRADE	
YEAR		PRICE	
FORMAT		LINER NOTES	

NOTES

RECORD DETAILS

ALBUM		CATALOG #	
ARTIST		LABEL	
COUNTRY		GRADE	
YEAR		PRICE	
FORMAT		LINER NOTES	

NOTES

RECORD DETAILS

ALBUM		CATALOG #	
ARTIST		LABEL	
COUNTRY		GRADE	
YEAR		PRICE	
FORMAT		LINER NOTES	

NOTES

RECORD DETAILS

ALBUM		CATALOG #	
ARTIST		LABEL	
COUNTRY		GRADE	
YEAR		PRICE	
FORMAT		LINER NOTES	

NOTES

RECORD DETAILS

ALBUM		CATALOG #	
ARTIST		LABEL	
COUNTRY		GRADE	
YEAR		PRICE	
FORMAT		LINER NOTES	

NOTES

RECORD DETAILS

ALBUM		CATALOG #	
ARTIST		LABEL	
COUNTRY		GRADE	
YEAR		PRICE	
FORMAT		LINER NOTES	

NOTES

RECORD DETAILS

ALBUM		CATALOG #	
ARTIST		LABEL	
COUNTRY		GRADE	
YEAR		PRICE	
FORMAT		LINER NOTES	

NOTES

RECORD DETAILS

ALBUM		CATALOG #	
ARTIST		LABEL	
COUNTRY		GRADE	
YEAR		PRICE	
FORMAT		LINER NOTES	

NOTES

RECORD DETAILS

ALBUM		CATALOG #	
ARTIST		LABEL	
COUNTRY		GRADE	
YEAR		PRICE	
FORMAT		LINER NOTES	

NOTES

RECORD DETAILS

ALBUM		CATALOG #	
ARTIST		LABEL	
COUNTRY		GRADE	
YEAR		PRICE	
FORMAT		LINER NOTES	

NOTES

RECORD DETAILS

ALBUM		CATALOG #	
ARTIST		LABEL	
COUNTRY		GRADE	
YEAR		PRICE	
FORMAT		LINER NOTES	

NOTES

RECORD DETAILS

ALBUM		CATALOG #	
ARTIST		LABEL	
COUNTRY		GRADE	
YEAR		PRICE	
FORMAT		LINER NOTES	

NOTES

RECORD DETAILS

ALBUM		CATALOG #	
ARTIST		LABEL	
COUNTRY		GRADE	
YEAR		PRICE	
FORMAT		LINER NOTES	

NOTES

RECORD DETAILS

ALBUM		CATALOG #	
ARTIST		LABEL	
COUNTRY		GRADE	
YEAR		PRICE	
FORMAT		LINER NOTES	

NOTES

RECORD DETAILS

ALBUM		CATALOG #	
ARTIST		LABEL	
COUNTRY		GRADE	
YEAR		PRICE	
FORMAT		LINER NOTES	

NOTES

RECORD DETAILS

ALBUM		CATALOG #	
ARTIST		LABEL	
COUNTRY		GRADE	
YEAR		PRICE	
FORMAT		LINER NOTES	

NOTES

RECORD DETAILS

ALBUM		CATALOG #	
ARTIST		LABEL	
COUNTRY		GRADE	
YEAR		PRICE	
FORMAT		LINER NOTES	

NOTES

RECORD DETAILS

ALBUM		CATALOG #	
ARTIST		LABEL	
COUNTRY		GRADE	
YEAR		PRICE	
FORMAT		LINER NOTES	

NOTES

RECORD DETAILS

ALBUM		CATALOG #	
ARTIST		LABEL	
COUNTRY		GRADE	
YEAR		PRICE	
FORMAT		LINER NOTES	

NOTES

RECORD DETAILS

ALBUM		CATALOG #	
ARTIST		LABEL	
COUNTRY		GRADE	
YEAR		PRICE	
FORMAT		LINER NOTES	

NOTES

RECORD DETAILS

ALBUM		CATALOG #	
ARTIST		LABEL	
COUNTRY		GRADE	
YEAR		PRICE	
FORMAT		LINER NOTES	

NOTES

RECORD DETAILS

ALBUM		CATALOG #	
ARTIST		LABEL	
COUNTRY		GRADE	
YEAR		PRICE	
FORMAT		LINER NOTES	

NOTES

RECORD DETAILS

ALBUM		CATALOG #	
ARTIST		LABEL	
COUNTRY		GRADE	
YEAR		PRICE	
FORMAT		LINER NOTES	

NOTES

RECORD DETAILS

ALBUM		CATALOG #	
ARTIST		LABEL	
COUNTRY		GRADE	
YEAR		PRICE	
FORMAT		LINER NOTES	

NOTES

RECORD DETAILS

ALBUM		CATALOG #	
ARTIST		LABEL	
COUNTRY		GRADE	
YEAR		PRICE	
FORMAT		LINER NOTES	

NOTES

RECORD DETAILS

ALBUM		CATALOG #	
ARTIST		LABEL	
COUNTRY		GRADE	
YEAR		PRICE	
FORMAT		LINER NOTES	

NOTES

RECORD DETAILS

ALBUM		CATALOG #	
ARTIST		LABEL	
COUNTRY		GRADE	
YEAR		PRICE	
FORMAT		LINER NOTES	

NOTES

RECORD DETAILS

ALBUM		CATALOG #	
ARTIST		LABEL	
COUNTRY		GRADE	
YEAR		PRICE	
FORMAT		LINER NOTES	

NOTES

RECORD DETAILS

ALBUM		CATALOG #	
ARTIST		LABEL	
COUNTRY		GRADE	
YEAR		PRICE	
FORMAT		LINER NOTES	

NOTES

RECORD DETAILS

ALBUM		CATALOG #	
ARTIST		LABEL	
COUNTRY		GRADE	
YEAR		PRICE	
FORMAT		LINER NOTES	

NOTES

RECORD DETAILS

ALBUM		CATALOG #	
ARTIST		LABEL	
COUNTRY		GRADE	
YEAR		PRICE	
FORMAT		LINER NOTES	

NOTES

RECORD DETAILS

ALBUM		CATALOG #	
ARTIST		LABEL	
COUNTRY		GRADE	
YEAR		PRICE	
FORMAT		LINER NOTES	

NOTES

RECORD DETAILS

ALBUM		CATALOG #	
ARTIST		LABEL	
COUNTRY		GRADE	
YEAR		PRICE	
FORMAT		LINER NOTES	

NOTES

RECORD DETAILS

ALBUM		CATALOG #	
ARTIST		LABEL	
COUNTRY		GRADE	
YEAR		PRICE	
FORMAT		LINER NOTES	

NOTES

RECORD DETAILS

ALBUM		CATALOG #	
ARTIST		LABEL	
COUNTRY		GRADE	
YEAR		PRICE	
FORMAT		LINER NOTES	

NOTES

RECORD DETAILS

ALBUM		CATALOG #	
ARTIST		LABEL	
COUNTRY		GRADE	
YEAR		PRICE	
FORMAT		LINER NOTES	

NOTES

RECORD DETAILS

ALBUM		CATALOG #	
ARTIST		LABEL	
COUNTRY		GRADE	
YEAR		PRICE	
FORMAT		LINER NOTES	

NOTES

RECORD DETAILS

ALBUM		CATALOG #	
ARTIST		LABEL	
COUNTRY		GRADE	
YEAR		PRICE	
FORMAT		LINER NOTES	

NOTES

RECORD DETAILS

ALBUM		CATALOG #	
ARTIST		LABEL	
COUNTRY		GRADE	
YEAR		PRICE	
FORMAT		LINER NOTES	

NOTES

RECORD DETAILS

ALBUM		CATALOG #	
ARTIST		LABEL	
COUNTRY		GRADE	
YEAR		PRICE	
FORMAT		LINER NOTES	

NOTES

RECORD DETAILS

ALBUM		CATALOG #	
ARTIST		LABEL	
COUNTRY		GRADE	
YEAR		PRICE	
FORMAT		LINER NOTES	

NOTES

RECORD DETAILS

ALBUM		CATALOG #	
ARTIST		LABEL	
COUNTRY		GRADE	
YEAR		PRICE	
FORMAT		LINER NOTES	

NOTES

RECORD DETAILS

ALBUM		CATALOG #	
ARTIST		LABEL	
COUNTRY		GRADE	
YEAR		PRICE	
FORMAT		LINER NOTES	

NOTES

RECORD DETAILS

ALBUM		CATALOG #	
ARTIST		LABEL	
COUNTRY		GRADE	
YEAR		PRICE	
FORMAT		LINER NOTES	

NOTES

RECORD DETAILS

ALBUM		CATALOG #	
ARTIST		LABEL	
COUNTRY		GRADE	
YEAR		PRICE	
FORMAT		LINER NOTES	

NOTES

RECORD DETAILS

ALBUM		CATALOG #	
ARTIST		LABEL	
COUNTRY		GRADE	
YEAR		PRICE	
FORMAT		LINER NOTES	

NOTES

RECORD DETAILS

ALBUM		CATALOG #	
ARTIST		LABEL	
COUNTRY		GRADE	
YEAR		PRICE	
FORMAT		LINER NOTES	

NOTES

RECORD DETAILS

ALBUM		CATALOG #	
ARTIST		LABEL	
COUNTRY		GRADE	
YEAR		PRICE	
FORMAT		LINER NOTES	

NOTES

RECORD DETAILS

ALBUM		CATALOG #	
ARTIST		LABEL	
COUNTRY		GRADE	
YEAR		PRICE	
FORMAT		LINER NOTES	

NOTES

RECORD DETAILS

ALBUM		CATALOG #	
ARTIST		LABEL	
COUNTRY		GRADE	
YEAR		PRICE	
FORMAT		LINER NOTES	

NOTES

RECORD DETAILS

ALBUM		CATALOG #	
ARTIST		LABEL	
COUNTRY		GRADE	
YEAR		PRICE	
FORMAT		LINER NOTES	

NOTES

RECORD DETAILS

ALBUM		CATALOG #	
ARTIST		LABEL	
COUNTRY		GRADE	
YEAR		PRICE	
FORMAT		LINER NOTES	

NOTES

RECORD DETAILS

ALBUM		CATALOG #	
ARTIST		LABEL	
COUNTRY		GRADE	
YEAR		PRICE	
FORMAT		LINER NOTES	

NOTES

RECORD DETAILS

ALBUM		CATALOG #	
ARTIST		LABEL	
COUNTRY		GRADE	
YEAR		PRICE	
FORMAT		LINER NOTES	

NOTES

RECORD DETAILS

ALBUM		CATALOG #	
ARTIST		LABEL	
COUNTRY		GRADE	
YEAR		PRICE	
FORMAT		LINER NOTES	

NOTES

RECORD DETAILS

ALBUM		CATALOG #	
ARTIST		LABEL	
COUNTRY		GRADE	
YEAR		PRICE	
FORMAT		LINER NOTES	

NOTES

RECORD DETAILS

ALBUM		CATALOG #	
ARTIST		LABEL	
COUNTRY		GRADE	
YEAR		PRICE	
FORMAT		LINER NOTES	

NOTES

RECORD DETAILS

ALBUM		CATALOG #	
ARTIST		LABEL	
COUNTRY		GRADE	
YEAR		PRICE	
FORMAT		LINER NOTES	

NOTES

RECORD DETAILS

ALBUM		CATALOG #	
ARTIST		LABEL	
COUNTRY		GRADE	
YEAR		PRICE	
FORMAT		LINER NOTES	

NOTES

RECORD DETAILS

ALBUM		CATALOG #	
ARTIST		LABEL	
COUNTRY		GRADE	
YEAR		PRICE	
FORMAT		LINER NOTES	

NOTES

RECORD DETAILS

ALBUM		CATALOG #	
ARTIST		LABEL	
COUNTRY		GRADE	
YEAR		PRICE	
FORMAT		LINER NOTES	

NOTES

RECORD DETAILS

ALBUM		CATALOG #	
ARTIST		LABEL	
COUNTRY		GRADE	
YEAR		PRICE	
FORMAT		LINER NOTES	

NOTES

RECORD DETAILS

ALBUM		CATALOG #	
ARTIST		LABEL	
COUNTRY		GRADE	
YEAR		PRICE	
FORMAT		LINER NOTES	

NOTES

RECORD DETAILS

ALBUM		CATALOG #	
ARTIST		LABEL	
COUNTRY		GRADE	
YEAR		PRICE	
FORMAT		LINER NOTES	

NOTES

RECORD DETAILS

ALBUM		CATALOG #	
ARTIST		LABEL	
COUNTRY		GRADE	
YEAR		PRICE	
FORMAT		LINER NOTES	

NOTES

RECORD DETAILS

ALBUM		CATALOG #	
ARTIST		LABEL	
COUNTRY		GRADE	
YEAR		PRICE	
FORMAT		LINER NOTES	

NOTES

RECORD DETAILS

ALBUM		CATALOG #	
ARTIST		LABEL	
COUNTRY		GRADE	
YEAR		PRICE	
FORMAT		LINER NOTES	

NOTES

RECORD DETAILS

ALBUM		CATALOG #	
ARTIST		LABEL	
COUNTRY		GRADE	
YEAR		PRICE	
FORMAT		LINER NOTES	

NOTES

RECORD DETAILS

ALBUM		CATALOG #	
ARTIST		LABEL	
COUNTRY		GRADE	
YEAR		PRICE	
FORMAT		LINER NOTES	

NOTES

RECORD DETAILS

ALBUM		CATALOG #	
ARTIST		LABEL	
COUNTRY		GRADE	
YEAR		PRICE	
FORMAT		LINER NOTES	

NOTES

RECORD DETAILS

ALBUM		CATALOG #	
ARTIST		LABEL	
COUNTRY		GRADE	
YEAR		PRICE	
FORMAT		LINER NOTES	

NOTES

RECORD DETAILS

ALBUM		CATALOG #	
ARTIST		LABEL	
COUNTRY		GRADE	
YEAR		PRICE	
FORMAT		LINER NOTES	

NOTES

RECORD DETAILS

ALBUM		CATALOG #	
ARTIST		LABEL	
COUNTRY		GRADE	
YEAR		PRICE	
FORMAT		LINER NOTES	

NOTES

RECORD DETAILS

ALBUM		CATALOG #	
ARTIST		LABEL	
COUNTRY		GRADE	
YEAR		PRICE	
FORMAT		LINER NOTES	

NOTES

RECORD DETAILS

ALBUM		CATALOG #	
ARTIST		LABEL	
COUNTRY		GRADE	
YEAR		PRICE	
FORMAT		LINER NOTES	

NOTES

RECORD DETAILS

ALBUM		CATALOG #	
ARTIST		LABEL	
COUNTRY		GRADE	
YEAR		PRICE	
FORMAT		LINER NOTES	

NOTES

RECORD DETAILS

ALBUM		CATALOG #	
ARTIST		LABEL	
COUNTRY		GRADE	
YEAR		PRICE	
FORMAT		LINER NOTES	

NOTES

RECORD DETAILS

ALBUM		CATALOG #	
ARTIST		LABEL	
COUNTRY		GRADE	
YEAR		PRICE	
FORMAT		LINER NOTES	

NOTES

RECORD DETAILS

ALBUM		CATALOG #	
ARTIST		LABEL	
COUNTRY		GRADE	
YEAR		PRICE	
FORMAT		LINER NOTES	

NOTES

RECORD DETAILS

ALBUM		CATALOG #	
ARTIST		LABEL	
COUNTRY		GRADE	
YEAR		PRICE	
FORMAT		LINER NOTES	

NOTES

RECORD DETAILS

ALBUM		CATALOG #	
ARTIST		LABEL	
COUNTRY		GRADE	
YEAR		PRICE	
FORMAT		LINER NOTES	

NOTES

RECORD DETAILS

ALBUM		CATALOG #	
ARTIST		LABEL	
COUNTRY		GRADE	
YEAR		PRICE	
FORMAT		LINER NOTES	

NOTES

RECORD DETAILS

ALBUM		CATALOG #	
ARTIST		LABEL	
COUNTRY		GRADE	
YEAR		PRICE	
FORMAT		LINER NOTES	

NOTES

RECORD DETAILS

ALBUM		CATALOG #	
ARTIST		LABEL	
COUNTRY		GRADE	
YEAR		PRICE	
FORMAT		LINER NOTES	

NOTES

RECORD DETAILS

ALBUM		CATALOG #	
ARTIST		LABEL	
COUNTRY		GRADE	
YEAR		PRICE	
FORMAT		LINER NOTES	

NOTES

RECORD DETAILS

ALBUM		CATALOG #	
ARTIST		LABEL	
COUNTRY		GRADE	
YEAR		PRICE	
FORMAT		LINER NOTES	

NOTES

RECORD DETAILS

ALBUM		CATALOG #	
ARTIST		LABEL	
COUNTRY		GRADE	
YEAR		PRICE	
FORMAT		LINER NOTES	

NOTES

RECORD DETAILS

ALBUM		CATALOG #	
ARTIST		LABEL	
COUNTRY		GRADE	
YEAR		PRICE	
FORMAT		LINER NOTES	

NOTES

RECORD DETAILS

ALBUM		CATALOG #	
ARTIST		LABEL	
COUNTRY		GRADE	
YEAR		PRICE	
FORMAT		LINER NOTES	

NOTES

RECORD DETAILS

ALBUM		CATALOG #	
ARTIST		LABEL	
COUNTRY		GRADE	
YEAR		PRICE	
FORMAT		LINER NOTES	

NOTES

RECORD DETAILS

ALBUM		CATALOG #	
ARTIST		LABEL	
COUNTRY		GRADE	
YEAR		PRICE	
FORMAT		LINER NOTES	

NOTES

RECORD DETAILS

ALBUM		CATALOG #	
ARTIST		LABEL	
COUNTRY		GRADE	
YEAR		PRICE	
FORMAT		LINER NOTES	

NOTES

RECORD DETAILS

ALBUM		CATALOG #	
ARTIST		LABEL	
COUNTRY		GRADE	
YEAR		PRICE	
FORMAT		LINER NOTES	

NOTES

RECORD DETAILS

ALBUM		CATALOG #	
ARTIST		LABEL	
COUNTRY		GRADE	
YEAR		PRICE	
FORMAT		LINER NOTES	

NOTES

RECORD DETAILS

ALBUM		CATALOG #	
ARTIST		LABEL	
COUNTRY		GRADE	
YEAR		PRICE	
FORMAT		LINER NOTES	

NOTES

RECORD DETAILS

ALBUM		CATALOG #	
ARTIST		LABEL	
COUNTRY		GRADE	
YEAR		PRICE	
FORMAT		LINER NOTES	

NOTES

RECORD DETAILS

ALBUM		CATALOG #	
ARTIST		LABEL	
COUNTRY		GRADE	
YEAR		PRICE	
FORMAT		LINER NOTES	

NOTES

RECORD DETAILS

ALBUM		CATALOG #	
ARTIST		LABEL	
COUNTRY		GRADE	
YEAR		PRICE	
FORMAT		LINER NOTES	

NOTES

RECORD DETAILS

ALBUM		CATALOG #	
ARTIST		LABEL	
COUNTRY		GRADE	
YEAR		PRICE	
FORMAT		LINER NOTES	

NOTES

RECORD DETAILS

ALBUM		CATALOG #	
ARTIST		LABEL	
COUNTRY		GRADE	
YEAR		PRICE	
FORMAT		LINER NOTES	

NOTES

RECORD DETAILS

ALBUM		CATALOG #	
ARTIST		LABEL	
COUNTRY		GRADE	
YEAR		PRICE	
FORMAT		LINER NOTES	

NOTES

RECORD DETAILS

ALBUM		CATALOG #	
ARTIST		LABEL	
COUNTRY		GRADE	
YEAR		PRICE	
FORMAT		LINER NOTES	

NOTES

RECORD DETAILS

ALBUM		CATALOG #	
ARTIST		LABEL	
COUNTRY		GRADE	
YEAR		PRICE	
FORMAT		LINER NOTES	

NOTES

RECORD DETAILS

ALBUM		CATALOG #	
ARTIST		LABEL	
COUNTRY		GRADE	
YEAR		PRICE	
FORMAT		LINER NOTES	

NOTES

RECORD DETAILS

ALBUM		CATALOG #	
ARTIST		LABEL	
COUNTRY		GRADE	
YEAR		PRICE	
FORMAT		LINER NOTES	

NOTES

RECORD DETAILS

ALBUM		CATALOG #	
ARTIST		LABEL	
COUNTRY		GRADE	
YEAR		PRICE	
FORMAT		LINER NOTES	

NOTES

RECORD DETAILS

ALBUM		CATALOG #	
ARTIST		LABEL	
COUNTRY		GRADE	
YEAR		PRICE	
FORMAT		LINER NOTES	

NOTES

RECORD DETAILS

ALBUM		CATALOG #	
ARTIST		LABEL	
COUNTRY		GRADE	
YEAR		PRICE	
FORMAT		LINER NOTES	

NOTES

RECORD DETAILS

ALBUM		CATALOG #	
ARTIST		LABEL	
COUNTRY		GRADE	
YEAR		PRICE	
FORMAT		LINER NOTES	

NOTES

RECORD DETAILS

ALBUM		CATALOG #	
ARTIST		LABEL	
COUNTRY		GRADE	
YEAR		PRICE	
FORMAT		LINER NOTES	

NOTES

RECORD DETAILS

ALBUM		CATALOG #	
ARTIST		LABEL	
COUNTRY		GRADE	
YEAR		PRICE	
FORMAT		LINER NOTES	

NOTES

RECORD DETAILS

ALBUM		CATALOG #	
ARTIST		LABEL	
COUNTRY		GRADE	
YEAR		PRICE	
FORMAT		LINER NOTES	

NOTES

RECORD DETAILS

ALBUM		CATALOG #	
ARTIST		LABEL	
COUNTRY		GRADE	
YEAR		PRICE	
FORMAT		LINER NOTES	

NOTES

RECORD DETAILS

ALBUM		CATALOG #	
ARTIST		LABEL	
COUNTRY		GRADE	
YEAR		PRICE	
FORMAT		LINER NOTES	

NOTES

RECORD DETAILS

ALBUM		CATALOG #	
ARTIST		LABEL	
COUNTRY		GRADE	
YEAR		PRICE	
FORMAT		LINER NOTES	

NOTES

RECORD DETAILS

ALBUM		CATALOG #	
ARTIST		LABEL	
COUNTRY		GRADE	
YEAR		PRICE	
FORMAT		LINER NOTES	

NOTES

RECORD DETAILS

ALBUM		CATALOG #	
ARTIST		LABEL	
COUNTRY		GRADE	
YEAR		PRICE	
FORMAT		LINER NOTES	

NOTES

RECORD DETAILS

ALBUM		CATALOG #	
ARTIST		LABEL	
COUNTRY		GRADE	
YEAR		PRICE	
FORMAT		LINER NOTES	

NOTES

RECORD DETAILS

ALBUM		CATALOG #	
ARTIST		LABEL	
COUNTRY		GRADE	
YEAR		PRICE	
FORMAT		LINER NOTES	

NOTES

RECORD DETAILS

ALBUM		CATALOG #	
ARTIST		LABEL	
COUNTRY		GRADE	
YEAR		PRICE	
FORMAT		LINER NOTES	

NOTES

RECORD DETAILS

ALBUM		CATALOG #	
ARTIST		LABEL	
COUNTRY		GRADE	
YEAR		PRICE	
FORMAT		LINER NOTES	

NOTES

RECORD DETAILS

ALBUM		CATALOG #	
ARTIST		LABEL	
COUNTRY		GRADE	
YEAR		PRICE	
FORMAT		LINER NOTES	

NOTES

RECORD DETAILS

ALBUM		CATALOG #	
ARTIST		LABEL	
COUNTRY		GRADE	
YEAR		PRICE	
FORMAT		LINER NOTES	

NOTES

RECORD DETAILS

ALBUM		CATALOG #	
ARTIST		LABEL	
COUNTRY		GRADE	
YEAR		PRICE	
FORMAT		LINER NOTES	

NOTES

RECORD DETAILS

ALBUM		CATALOG #	
ARTIST		LABEL	
COUNTRY		GRADE	
YEAR		PRICE	
FORMAT		LINER NOTES	

NOTES

RECORD DETAILS

ALBUM		CATALOG #	
ARTIST		LABEL	
COUNTRY		GRADE	
YEAR		PRICE	
FORMAT		LINER NOTES	

NOTES

RECORD DETAILS

ALBUM		CATALOG #	
ARTIST		LABEL	
COUNTRY		GRADE	
YEAR		PRICE	
FORMAT		LINER NOTES	

NOTES

RECORD DETAILS

ALBUM		CATALOG #	
ARTIST		LABEL	
COUNTRY		GRADE	
YEAR		PRICE	
FORMAT		LINER NOTES	

NOTES

RECORD DETAILS

ALBUM		CATALOG #	
ARTIST		LABEL	
COUNTRY		GRADE	
YEAR		PRICE	
FORMAT		LINER NOTES	

NOTES

RECORD DETAILS

ALBUM		CATALOG #	
ARTIST		LABEL	
COUNTRY		GRADE	
YEAR		PRICE	
FORMAT		LINER NOTES	

NOTES

RECORD DETAILS

ALBUM		CATALOG #	
ARTIST		LABEL	
COUNTRY		GRADE	
YEAR		PRICE	
FORMAT		LINER NOTES	

NOTES

RECORD DETAILS

ALBUM		CATALOG #	
ARTIST		LABEL	
COUNTRY		GRADE	
YEAR		PRICE	
FORMAT		LINER NOTES	

NOTES

RECORD DETAILS

ALBUM		CATALOG #	
ARTIST		LABEL	
COUNTRY		GRADE	
YEAR		PRICE	
FORMAT		LINER NOTES	

NOTES

RECORD DETAILS

ALBUM		CATALOG #	
ARTIST		LABEL	
COUNTRY		GRADE	
YEAR		PRICE	
FORMAT		LINER NOTES	

NOTES

RECORD DETAILS

ALBUM		CATALOG #	
ARTIST		LABEL	
COUNTRY		GRADE	
YEAR		PRICE	
FORMAT		LINER NOTES	

NOTES

RECORD DETAILS

ALBUM		CATALOG #	
ARTIST		LABEL	
COUNTRY		GRADE	
YEAR		PRICE	
FORMAT		LINER NOTES	

NOTES

RECORD DETAILS

ALBUM		CATALOG #	
ARTIST		LABEL	
COUNTRY		GRADE	
YEAR		PRICE	
FORMAT		LINER NOTES	

NOTES

RECORD DETAILS

ALBUM		CATALOG #	
ARTIST		LABEL	
COUNTRY		GRADE	
YEAR		PRICE	
FORMAT		LINER NOTES	

NOTES

RECORD DETAILS

ALBUM		CATALOG #	
ARTIST		LABEL	
COUNTRY		GRADE	
YEAR		PRICE	
FORMAT		LINER NOTES	

NOTES

RECORD DETAILS

ALBUM		CATALOG #	
ARTIST		LABEL	
COUNTRY		GRADE	
YEAR		PRICE	
FORMAT		LINER NOTES	

NOTES

RECORD DETAILS

ALBUM		CATALOG #	
ARTIST		LABEL	
COUNTRY		GRADE	
YEAR		PRICE	
FORMAT		LINER NOTES	

NOTES

RECORD DETAILS

ALBUM		CATALOG #	
ARTIST		LABEL	
COUNTRY		GRADE	
YEAR		PRICE	
FORMAT		LINER NOTES	

NOTES

RECORD DETAILS

ALBUM		CATALOG #	
ARTIST		LABEL	
COUNTRY		GRADE	
YEAR		PRICE	
FORMAT		LINER NOTES	

NOTES

RECORD DETAILS

ALBUM		CATALOG #	
ARTIST		LABEL	
COUNTRY		GRADE	
YEAR		PRICE	
FORMAT		LINER NOTES	

NOTES

RECORD DETAILS

ALBUM		CATALOG #	
ARTIST		LABEL	
COUNTRY		GRADE	
YEAR		PRICE	
FORMAT		LINER NOTES	

NOTES

RECORD DETAILS

ALBUM		CATALOG #	
ARTIST		LABEL	
COUNTRY		GRADE	
YEAR		PRICE	
FORMAT		LINER NOTES	

NOTES

RECORD DETAILS

ALBUM		CATALOG #	
ARTIST		LABEL	
COUNTRY		GRADE	
YEAR		PRICE	
FORMAT		LINER NOTES	

NOTES

RECORD DETAILS

ALBUM		CATALOG #	
ARTIST		LABEL	
COUNTRY		GRADE	
YEAR		PRICE	
FORMAT		LINER NOTES	

NOTES

CPSIA information can be obtained
at www.ICGtesting.com
Printed in the USA
BVHW041348140422
634332BV00016B/946

9 781953 557650